FALLA

2 DANZAS ESPAÑOLAS "LA VIDA BREVE"
Original Piano Solo Version

ファリャ　スペイン舞曲 第1番・第2番《はかなき人生》より
作曲者によるピアノ版

Edited with commentary by Takejiro Hirai and Rie Hirai

校訂・解説 —— 平井丈二郎
平井李枝

全音楽譜出版社

序

　マヌエル・デ・ファリャ（1876 - 1946）は20世紀スペイン近代音楽を代表する三大作曲家の一人である。ピアニストとしても活躍していたファリャであるが、その作品はピアノ独奏用にとどまらず、歌曲、ギター、室内楽、オーケストラ、協奏曲、そしてサルスエラや人形劇、オペラ、バレエといった舞台音楽に至るまで多彩なジャンルを網羅している。

　ファリャは、フラメンコなどスペイン民族音楽の特徴を作曲作品に取り入れ、スペイン的な情緒と歯切れのよいリズム感、斬新な和声で深く印象に残る作品を多く生み出した。民族音楽の特徴を生かしながらも、ロマンティックで趣のあるピアノ曲《4つのスペイン風小品》は初期の傑作である。

　そして、中期のピアノ曲で特筆すべきは《ベティカ幻想曲》であろう。この作品にはアンダルシアのフラメンコの要素がふんだんに盛り込まれており、ピアノ音楽でありながら舞踊や打楽器的な響きを持ち合わせる個性的で新しい書法が当時の音楽界で絶賛された。

　舞台音楽では、多彩なオーケストラ技法と、躍動感あふれるリズム、忘れ難いメロディーで聴衆を魅了した。バレエ音楽《恋は魔術師》、《三角帽子》、オペラ《はかなき人生》などは、ファリャを大作曲家として世間に知らしめた傑作である。これらの作品は、ファリャ自身によってピアノ独奏用に編曲されているため、多くのピアニストに愛奏されている。

　ファリャの強烈なリズム、情熱、刺激的な音響は、魔力的な音楽となって、今日も聴衆を惹きつけている。そしてスペイン人としての誇りと、類いまれなる音楽的センスによって、フラメンコを民族音楽から真の芸術音楽へと昇華させている。

　今回の出版にあたっては、ピアニストにとってより使いやすく、実用的な楽譜を目指して編纂を行っている。舞台音楽のピアノ独奏版においては、オリジナルであるオーケストラの響きを再現できるようなペダリングを表記した。

　本書によって、エキゾチックで魅惑的なファリャのピアニズムを存分に味わっていただき、多くの方に演奏していただければこの上ない幸せである。

2012年5月

平井丈二郎（ジュリアード音楽芸術博士）

平井李枝（音楽博士）

FOREWORD

Manuel de Falla (1876-1946) was one of the three great composers of modern Spanish music in 20th century, along with his seniors, Albeniz and Granados. Although he was known as a pianist, his compositions cover a wide range of genre; for piano, for vocal, guitar, chamber music, orchestra, concerto, and theatre music as zarzuela, puppet, opera, ballet.

Falla used characteristic idioms of Flamenco for his compositions. He created many works in a new style which has the atmosphere of Spanish folk music, lively rhythm, and innovative harmony.

The piano work, *4 piezas españolas* are the master works of his early period. It has a characteristic Spanish elements and a tasteful romanticism.

Fantasía Baetica, a master work of his middle age, in which he used a various elements of Flamenco. It has a new style of writing by Falla, combining highly virtuosic piano technique with elements of Flamenco dance and sound. It was highly esteemed by musical world.

The theatre music of Falla fascinated the audience by his colorful orchestration, lively rhythm and unforgettable melodies. The ballet music *El Amor Brujo (Love, the Magician)*, *El Sombrero de Tres Picos (Three Cornered Hat)* and the Opera *La Vida Breve* made him recognized as a great composer. These works are transcribed for piano solo by Falla himself and they became favorite of many pianists.

The impression of Falla's music can be described as a magical music of intence rhythm, passion, stimulating sound which attracts audience.
He sublimated the Flamenco from folk music to the musical art by his incredible sense of arts.

The present publication was edited for practical use by pianists and music lovers. For the piano version of theatre music, we wrote the pedal mark in order to reproduce a sonority of orchestra which Falla wanted.

It will be our pleasure if this publication helps the understanding of exotic and fascinating pianism of Falla.

May, 2012
Takejiro Takatomo HIRAI, DMA (Juilliard)
Rie HIRAI, Doctor of Music

Manuel de Falla (1876-1946)

CONTENTS●目次

2 Danzas Españolas
"La Vida Breve"

スペイン舞曲 第1番・第2番
オペラ《はかなき人生》より

●本書の編纂方針

◆テキスト

①楽譜のテキストは初版及びその再版によっており校訂者が加えたものはない。初版は当時の版下書式を用いているので、音楽的な内容を全く変えずに現代のスタイルに変更した。

②音符や臨時記号、スラー、タイなどで明らかに初版の版下ミスと思われるものは訂正、又は追加修正した。間違いかどうか明らかでないものは、その旨を註に記した。

③ファリャの和声は個性的且つ民族的であるため、臨時記号の読み違いが多いので、わかりやすく修正した。

◆運指

①運指は原則として校訂者によるものであり、作曲者自身の運指はイタリック体の数字で記し、校訂者によるものと区別した。

②原典版にある両手配分の指示は、L.H.（左手）及びR.H.（右手）に変換して記した。校訂者によるものは ⌊、⌉ または、(L.) (R.) で示した。

◆ペダル

①ペダル記号は原則として校訂者によるもので、作曲者の理想とした方式に基づいている。

②原典版に付されたペダルは Ped. の記号で記してあり、校訂者によるペダル指示 Ped. と区別した。勿論、ペダルの用法は状況により、又、好みによりかなり異なるものであり、すべてを満足させるペダルの用法を記すことは不可能に近い。しかし、正しいペダルの使い方は、ファリャの求めていたピアノの響きを再現するために不可欠であるので、本書では単純明快で音楽的に正しいペダル用法を記している。una corda、tre corde、及び u. c.、t. c. は、ほとんどの場合校訂者が補足したものである。原典版の 2Ped. は Ped. + u. c. を意味する。

◆メトロノーム表示

本書のメトロノーム表示は原典版による。

●ファリャ　その生涯と作品

　スペイン近代音楽を代表する作曲家、マヌエル・デ・ファリャ Manuel de Falla は 1876 年 11 月 23 日、スペインの南部、アンダルシアの港町のカディスに生まれた。父はバレンシア出身の実業家、ホセ・マリア José María de Falla Franco、母はフランスにほど近いカタルーニャ出身のマリア・ヘスス María Jesús Matheu。ファリャの本名は、マヌエル・マリア・デ・ロス・ドロルス・ファリャ・イ・マテウ Manuel María de los Dolors Falla y Matheu という長いものであった。ファリャには何人もの兄弟がいたが、無事に成長したのは弟ヘルマンと妹マリア・デル・カルメンのみであった。

　裕福な家庭に育ったファリャは、幼い頃、母や祖父に音楽の手ほどきを受けた。そして 9 才から本格的にピアノのレッスンを受けることになる。最初の師、エロイサ・ガリューゾはすぐに修道女になってしまったので続かなかったが、その後 13 才の頃からピアノをアレハンドロ・オデロに、和声と対位法をエンリケ・ブロカに師事する。

　15 才の頃は、友人らと文学雑誌を創刊するなど、ファリャの関心は文筆業とジャーナリズムにあった。

　1896 年頃から作曲に本格的に取り組み、《ノクターン》を作曲。これはカディスで 1899 年に初演された。1898 年、ファリャ一家は経済的な問題から完全にマドリードに移住し、ファリャはマドリード王立音楽院で当時の名教授として名高いホセ・トラゴ José Trago (1856-1934) にピアノを師事することになる。トラゴ教授は大変寛大で、作曲にも興味を持ち始めた若いピアニストを熱心にサポートした。

　23 才から彼は自分の名前に "de" を用い、Manuel de Falla と署名するようになる。1899 年から 1905 年にかけてスペインの民族的な要素がふんだんに盛り込まれたスペイン固有のオペラであるサルスエラをアマデオ・ヴィヴェスらとのコラボレーションにより 5 作品作曲した。

　1902 年から 1904 年、フェリペ・ペドレル Felipe Pedrell (1841-1922) に作曲を師事する。ペドレルは当時作曲家として著名であっただけでなく、スペイン民族音楽研究の第一人者としてマドリード音楽院で音楽史の教授をしていた。同門の先輩には、スペイン音楽を代表する先駆者、アルベニス、グラナドスらがいる。ファリャはペドレルからスペイン音楽史やスペインの民族音楽の様々な特徴や技法を習得した。

　ファリャの初期の作品はロマン主義的な雰囲気の強いものが多く見られる。しかし、ペドレルに師事してから後の作品にはスペインの民族音楽、特にアンダルシアのフラメンコからの音楽的要素を用いた作風が多く発表されるようになった。そしてそのような作品はスペインの聴衆に熱狂的に受け入れられるのであった。

　まず、1902 年にアンダルシア風な音楽語法で作曲された歌曲《おまえの黒い瞳》は、一般大衆に広く受け入れられ人気

を得た。そしてファリャが作曲家として一躍注目を浴びることとなるのが、1905年、27才の時に作曲されたオペラ《はかなき人生》である。アンダルシアの雰囲気がふんだんに取り入れられたこの作品は、マドリード王立音楽院主催の新作オペラコンテストに出品され一等賞となった。また、オペラ提出の翌日開催された同音楽院主催のピアノコンクールにおいてファリャは優勝する。この時2位になったのが、後にグラナドスの愛弟子としてバルセロナで教鞭をとるフランク・マーシャルであった。このコンクールを機に親友となったファリャとマーシャルの友情は生涯にわたって続くことになる。

《はかなき人生》はコンテストの優勝特典によりすぐに上演される約束になっていたが、残念なことになかなか果たされなかった。《はかなき人生》の上演を願うファリャは、1907年フランス・パリに渡り、《魔法使いの弟子》などで知られる作曲家ポール・デュカス Paul Dukas（1865-1935）に面会し、《はかなき人生》を聴いてもらうことができた。

デュカスは《はかなき人生》を大変気に入り、フランスのコミック座で上演できるように尽力した。感激したファリャは、デュカスに和声やオーケストレーション（管弦楽法）などの作曲法を師事することになる。デュカスの教えは、ファリャの舞台音楽作品に見られるダイナミックで色彩豊かなオーケストレーションの基礎となっているであろう。デュカスは作曲の指導だけでなく、友人のアルベニスを紹介するなど、ファリャの音楽家人生を切り開くための様々な手助けと後押しをした。そして、ドビュッシー、ラヴェル、アルベニス、ヴィニエス、ストラビンスキーら当時の巨匠らと親交を持つことになる。

1906年から構想を練り、パリ滞在中の1909年に完成したピアノ作品《4つのスペイン風小品》は、同郷の大先輩であるアルベニスに捧げられた。ロマンティックで香り豊かなこの作品はリカルド・ヴィニエスによってパリのサル・エラールで初演された。ヴィニエスはカタロニア出身のピアニストでラヴェルやドビュッシーのピアノ曲の初演を行うなど当時大活躍していた。

1913年オペラ《はかなき人生》はついに、フランスのニースで初演される。その後パリのコミック座、スペインのマドリードなどで次々に上演されることとなる。

1914年には、民族愛にあふれた歌曲集《7つのスペイン民謡》を発表。パリで充実した音楽生活を送っていたが、1915年、第一次世界大戦の開戦を受けてマドリードに戻る。1916年には戦争の影響で、先輩の作曲家、グラナドスが悲劇的な死を遂げるなど、彼にとってショックな出来事が多かった。しかし、当時スペインで大人気だった劇作家グレゴリオ・マルティネス・シエラ夫妻と出会い、2つの傑作バレエ作品《恋は魔術師》《三角帽子》を完成させる。

1915年《ヒタネリア》という題名で発表された舞台音楽は2年後に《恋は魔術師》という題でバレエ音楽として再発表される。フラメンコの民族性豊かな音楽的要素と色彩豊かな管弦楽法で情景を描写した傑作である。この作品は、ファリャによってピアノ独奏用にも編曲されており、特に〈火祭りの踊り〉などはルービンシュタインに愛奏されるなど、世界で愛好されている。

1915年、フランス時代から構想を練っていたピアノとオーケストラのための交響的印象《スペインの庭の夜》が完成。1916年4月にマドリードのレアル劇場で初演される。

1918年、ドビュッシーの死を悼んで作曲した《ドビュッシーの墓への讃歌》は、スペイン風の香りがする作品で、ドビュッシーが好んでいたギターのための曲として発表された。その後ピアノ曲になり、多くのピアニストに演奏されている。

1919年に完成した《三角帽子》は、ペドロ・アントニオ・デ・アラルコンによるスペインの民話を題材にしたバレエ音楽で、《恋は魔術師》と同じくマルティネス・シエラの台本による。初演は依頼主のディアギレフとロシアバレエ団、衣装や舞台装置のデザインにパブロ・ピカソ、指揮はエルネスト・アンセルメという豪華な顔ぶれで行われた。躍動感あふれる音楽とフラメンコの情緒が印象的なこの作品は、後にファリャ自身によってピアノソロ版に編曲され、多くのピアニストに愛奏されている。

1919年に作曲された《ベティカ幻想曲》、斬新な和声とアンダルシア・フラメンコの民族的なリズムが印象的なこの作品は、ピアニスト、アルトゥール・ルービンシュタインのために作曲され、翌年にニューヨークで初演された。

1922年、ファリャは1919年に初めて訪れて以来、大変気に入っていたグラナダのアルハンブラに移住する。この頃のファリャは特にフラメンコの歌のなかのカンテ・ホンドとよばれる歌い方に関心があり、アンダルシア出身でカンテ・ホンドの専門家で詩人のガルシア・ロルカ García Lorca（1898-1936）と親交を持った。カンテ・フラメンコの伝統が衰退するのを危惧して、ロルカとともに1922年に初めてのカンテ・ホンドのためのコンクールを主催するほどであった。

また同時期に、ファリャはハープシーコード奏者のワンダ・ランドフスカと出会う。1923年、ポリニャック公爵夫人の依頼により作曲された人形劇オペラ《ペドロ親方の人形芝居》を発表。この作品は、セルバンテスのドン・キホーテ第2部のエピソードをもとにファリャ自身が台本を書いた。オーケストラと独奏楽器にチェンバロ、ハープが用いられる珍しい編成となっており、初演にはランドフスカも関わっている。

その後、4年の歳月を費やした《ハープシコード協奏曲》が1926年に完成する。ランドフスカの委嘱によって作曲されたこの作品はバルセロナのカタロニア音楽堂で初演される。

1927年から1936年、ファリャの作品は極端に少なくなる。それは健康上の理由と、もうひとつ、《アトランティダ》という伝説の大陸の名を題名とするカタロニア語による大作のカンタータを作曲するために全精力を費やしていたこと

による。敬虔なクリスチャンであったファリャにとってミサ曲を書くことは生涯の望みであった。

1931年、共和制だったスペインに右翼の蜂起が起こり、グラナダにも不穏な空気が漂う。そして8月、大親友のガルシア・ロルカが右翼に突然拉致され、理由もなく銃殺されるというショッキングな事件が起きるのである。左翼的、または自由主義と思われる人物はことごとく連行されたので、ファリャは内戦が終わるまでひっそりと暮らしていた。その中で、尊敬する師であるポール・デュカスの死に際しては、ピアノ曲《ポール・デュカスの墓への讃歌》を作曲している。

1939年、ブエノスアイレスでの演奏会に招かれたファリャはアルゼンチンへ向けて出発した。そして二度と故郷に帰ることはなかった。アルゼンチンに移住したファリャは演奏活動を行い、コルドバ州のアルタ・グラシアの山荘で暮らす。妹のマリア・デル・カルメンが、生涯独身を貫いたファリャの世話を献身的にしていた。

1946年11月14日、ファリャは70才の誕生日を目前にして静かに亡くなった。ファリャの葬儀は生まれ故郷スペイン、カディスの大聖堂で厳かに行われた。ファリャの死によって未完となった《アトランティダ》は愛弟子エルネスト・ハルフテルによって完成され、1961年にバルセロナのリセウ劇場で初演された。死後もなお、ファリャが残した音楽は、スペインの民族性とクラシック音楽が魅惑的に融合した傑作として愛好され、その伝統はスペインのみならずラテンアメリカ音楽へと引き継がれている。

（平井李枝）

●曲目解説

スペイン舞曲 第1番・第2番
オペラ《はかなき人生》より

《はかなき人生》はファリャが27歳の1904年に作曲されたオペラ作品である。マドリードの王立音楽院が開催したスペイン語による新作オペラ作曲コンクールに出品されたこの作品は、並みいる強豪を抑え一等賞を獲得した。2幕4場からなる《はかなき人生》の台本は、サルスエラの脚本家として活躍していたカルロス・フェルナンデス・シャウによるもので、アンダルシアの方言が使われている。高い評価を得て優勝を勝ち取った《はかなき人生》は、残念なことにすぐに上演というわけにはいかなかった。新作オペラコンクールの優勝作品は、マドリード劇場ですぐに上演される約束であったが、それがなかなか果たされなかったのである。ファリャは自作オペラの上演を夢見て、1907年パリへ渡る。そしてポール・デュカスとの出会いが、この《はかなき人生》の初演

へと導くのである。デュカスは、スペインからやってきた若い作曲家の才能あふれる新作オペラに非常に感銘を受け、フランスのコミック座で上演できるよう尽力した。その結果、ついに1913年4月、ニースでフランス語版が初演される。その後1914年1月6日にパリのオペラ・コミック座で、さらに同年の11月14日にはスペイン・マドリードのサルスエラ劇場でスペイン語版が初演されるなど、ファリャが作曲家として一躍注目される作品となった。

《はかなき人生》は、スペインのグラナダを舞台に繰り広げられる身分違いの恋物語。身分の低いジプシー娘は、恋人が高貴な女性とこっそり結婚したことにショックを受け、死んでしまう。裏切り者の男もジプシー娘の大叔父によって殺されるという衝撃的な内容となっている。

第2幕に2つのスペイン舞曲が配置されている。第1番は第2幕第1場に登場する。豪華な館で繰り広げられる結婚の祝宴のフラメンコの歌と踊りである。この曲はオペラから独立して、オーケストラや吹奏楽、ギター、ヴァイオリン、チェロ、ピアノ連弾など、多種多様な編成で愛奏されている。特にクライスラーがヴァイオリン独奏用に編曲したものは有名である。

第2番は第2幕第2場の開始から演奏される。オペラではこの曲も結婚式の宴のシーンを表す華やかで活気のあるフラメンコ音楽である。フラメンコの歌手（カンタオール）も登場して演奏される。この曲は第1番に比べると演奏される機会は少ないが、コブシの効いたメロディーと、歯切れの良いリズム、掛け声や手拍子など、アンダルシア民族を代表するフラメンコの魅力的な部分が存分に発揮された非常に演奏効果のある作品となっている。

本書の出版にあたっては、世界に出回っている初版およびそのリプリントに見られる音符や表記に関する疑問点を解決するため、1913年にパリのMax Eschig社から出版されたオペラ《はかなき人生》のヴォーカルスコアをもとに編纂を行った。

（平井李枝）

●演奏にあたって

スペイン舞曲 第1番

《はかなき人生》のスペイン舞曲第1番は、ファリャが音楽界で国際的に知られるようになったきっかけの作品と言えるだろう。この曲は、オリジナルのオーケストラ版、ピアノソロ版に加え、吹奏楽、ギター、ヴァイオリン、チェロ、ピアノデュオ（2台ピアノと4手の両方）など様々な楽器のために編曲されている。最も有名なのは、フリッツ・クライスラーによるヴァイオリンとピアノのための編曲で、たくさんのヴァイオリニストによって演奏されている。

主題は、速いテンポの3/8拍子のフラメンコ舞踊のスタイルで書かれている。演奏を通して、カスタネットやフラメンコダンサーの足を踏み鳴らすサパテアードの音を聞くことができるだろう。右手のトレモロはノンレガートで演奏し、4小節間の前奏では、左手のスタッカートは非常に鋭く弾かなければならない。主題は正確なテンポ感の中で、はっきりとした音色で歌って演奏したい。

第49小節からはペダルを使用しないか、ほんの少しだけ使うに止め、ノンレガートで演奏して欲しい。

第96小節から対位法的になるが、ペダルは少ししか使用しないように。

第115小節からの**Pesante**と表記された箇所では、テンポが幅広くなり、カンテ・ホンドの歌い手が登場する。主題は腕全体を使って、丸く太い音色で演奏してほしい。

曲全体を通して、小さい音符は演奏しなくても差し支えない。

スペイン舞曲 第2番

この舞曲は、全体を通して主にヘミオラのクロスリズムが用いられるスタイルの3/4拍子で書かれている。左手が広い音域を動くため、この作品ではペダルの性能を充分に活用することが大切である。この作品全体で使用されているシンコペーションのリズムが、揺れ動きを作り出している。

二重音の音階はノンレガートで演奏されることをお勧めしたい。左手から対位法の旋律を引き出したい。

第47小節目の**Poco Animato**と表記された箇所からは、オクターブのユニゾンで合唱隊のコーラスが表われる。このオクターブは𝆑でたっぷりとした音色で歌い、さらにそれがヘミオラのリズムを作り出していることに注意して演奏してほしい。

第229小節からはクロスリズムがあらわれる。右手が通常の3/4拍子、左手がヘミオラとなっている。フラメンコの踊りは徐々に速度を増し、終わりに向かって音量も大きくなり高揚していく。

（平井丈二郎・平井李枝）

10

● Editorial Notes

◆ Text

1. The present edition is based on the original edition and its reprints. No addition to the text has been made by the editors. Since the original edition mostly uses a notation style of engraving, we changed into a modern style without any change of musical contents.

2. The notes, accidentals, slurs and ties which the editors consider apparent misprints, have been corrected or added by the editors. For those which are questionable are indicated by footnotes.

3. Since Falla's harmony is very individual and based on Spanish folklore music, there are reading mistakes very often. Therefore, the editors added a considerable amount of precautionary accidentals to the text.

◆ Fingering

1. Fingerings in this edition are almost exclusively by the editors. However, although rare, the original fingerings, found in the first edition, are retained in this edition in italic numerals.

2. Original hand distributions are retained in this edition using L.H., R.H., Cf. (L.),(R.) or ⌊ , ⌉ = by the editors.

◆ Pedaling

1. This edition is the first publication to include pedal indications by the editors which are based on the modern method.

2. In a very few places where original pedal marks are found in the first edition, the editors retained these marks by using ℒ℘. marks. Cf. ℛ. =by the editors.

The use of pedal differs by the situation and the personal taste, so that it is almost impossible to write out the pedal indications which satisfy all these situations. However, the use of the pedal in the right place is also indispensable in order to obtain sonorities which Falla wanted to create.

The editors use the simplest and clearest way of pedaling yet musically acceptable.

una corda, *tre corde*, *u. c.*, *t. c.*, are mostly by the editors.

◆ Metronomic indications

Metronomic indications in this edition are mainly original.

● Manuel de Falla

Life and Works

The Great modern Spanish composer, Manuel de Falla was born on November 23, 1876 in Cadiz, Andalusian port town of southern Spain. Father of Falla was a businessman, José María de Falla, born in Valencia. Mother was María Jesús Matheu, born in Catalonia. His complete name was incredibly long; Manuel María de los Dolors Falla y Matheu. He had many brothers but only brother Germán and sister Maria del Carmen survived

Falla grew up in a wealthy family, received his early musical education from his mother and grandfather. At 9 years old, he started taking piano lessons with Eloísa Galluzo. But it was soon ended after she entered a convent, Sister of Charity. At 13 years old, he continued piano lessons with Alejandro Odero. He also studied the techniques of harmony and counterpoint from Enrique Broca.

At age 15, Falla was interested in literature and journalism. He founded the magazine with his friends.

In 1896, Falla started to compose seriously, writing *Nocturno* for piano solo. It was premiered in Cadiz 1899. In 1898, family of Falla moved to Madrid due to economical problem. Falla studied piano with José Trago, who was a renowned professor in Conservatory of Madrid. Prof. Trago was a very generous teacher, he supported young pianist Falla to get into composition beside piano study.

At age 23, Falla started to use "de" with his surname: Manuel de Falla. In 1899 to 1905, Falla composed 5 zarzuelas, collaborated with dramatist Amadeo Vivas etc. Zarzuela is a kind of theater music, like opera or operetta, indigenous to Spain which incorporate plentiful material of Spanish folklore.

In 1902 to 1904, he studied composition with Felipe Pedrell. Pedrell was not only a prominent composer but also a leading researcher of Spanish folk music, teaching history of music at Conservatory of Madrid. Prominent composers, Isaac Albeniz and Enrique Granados were his senior students of Pedrell. Falla acquired the history of Spanish music, character and musical technique of Spanish folk music with Pedrell.

The early works of Falla have atmosphere of romanticism. After studying with Pedrell, he used characteristics of Spanish musical idioms into his new works. *Tus ojillos negro* for vocal and piano was composed in 1909, using Andalusian musical idioms, especially Flamenco. It became popular among common people of Spain.

Falla garnered attention as a promising young composer by his opera *La vida breve*, which composed in 1905, at age 27. He submitted opera for the competition of new opera in

Madrid, it was highly praised by judges and won the first prize. He also won first prize in the piano contest of Madrid conservatory, the following day of his opera score was submitted. Second prize was Frank Marshall who teaches in Barcelona a few years later as a favorite disciple of Granados. Taking this opportunity, Falla and Marshall became a close friend during their lifetime.

La vida breve was promised to premiere soon as champion's privilege, but unfortunately it was not realized. Therefore he went to Paris hoping the premiere of his opera to be realized. there he met Paul Dukas, who was a well-known composer for symphonic poem; *The Sorcerer's Apprentice*. Falla played his opera *La vida breve*.

Dukas was very interested in young composer's Spanish opera and he had exerted himself to premiere Falla's opera at Theatre Comic of France. Falla was deeply moved by Dukas' kindness, he started to study harmony and orchestration with maestro Dukas. Falla's dynamic and colorful orchestrations of his theatre music are based on the teaching of Dukas. Dukas not only advised on composing but also introduced to his friend, Albeniz, helping Falla's musical career. In Paris, Falla acquainted with leading musicians at that time; Claude Debussy, Maurice Ravel, Isaac Albeniz, Ricardo Viñes and Igor Stravinsky.

In 1909, Falla completed the piano work *4 piezas españolas* which he developed the ideas since1906, and dedicated to Issac Albeniz. Premiered by Ricardo Viñes, a great Catalonian pianist, who premieres almost all of Debussy and Ravel's piano works at that time.

In 1913, *La vida breve* was at last premiered at the theatre in Nice of France. Soon after it was presented at Opera Comic in Paris and in Madrid, Spain.

In 1914, Falla composed *Siete canciones populares españolas* which contains full of love for Falla's native district, Andalusia. Falla had a full and enriching life in Paris, but he returned to Madrid caused by World War I broke out. Falla had many shocking problems at that time. In 1916, his respectful senior, Enrique Granados died tragically in an accident caused by this War. Falla devoted himself to compose. He met Martines Sierra, who was the well known librettist in Spain. Falla composed 2 master works for ballet, *El Amor Brujo (Love, the Magician)*, and *El sombrero de tres picos (Three-Cornered Hat)*, in collaboration with Sierra. Falla composed theatre music for Flamenco, Gitaneria. 2 years later, he transformed this work as a ballet music, *El Amor Brujo*. This is one of his master works based on Andalusian nationalism such as elements of Flamenco and colorful dramatic orchestration. This work was revised for piano solo by composer himself. Especially *Ritual Fire Dance* became popular all over the world among music lovers by a remarkable performance of pianist Artur Rubinstein.

In 1915, Falla completed a composition, in the style of symphonic poem for piano and orchestra, *Noches en los jardin de España* which had been elaborated a plan since Paris period. It was dedicated to Ricardo Viñes, premiered in April 1916 at Teatre Real Madrid.

In 1918, he composed *Homenaje: pour Le tombeau de Claude Debussy* for paying respect to the death of Debussy. This work was composed for guitar but later it was revised for piano solo by Falla.

In 1919, Falla finished work for ballet *El sombrero de tres picos*. The story was based on Spanish folktale by Pedro Antonio de Alarcón, libretto was written by Martines Sierra, same as *El Amor Brujo*. The commissioner of this work was Serge Diaguilev and Ballet Russia.

Premiered in September 22,1919 at Alhambra Theatre, the member was incredible as follows. Producer: Diaguilev, Choreography: Léonide Massine, Dance: Ballet Russia, Conductor: Ernest Ansermet, Designer of stage scenery and costumes: great painter, Pablo Picasso. This work became popular all over the world for vivid rhythm and emotional exoticism of Flamenco. Soon the work was revised for piano solo by Falla, and loved by great pianists and music lovers.

A large-scale piano work, *Fantasía Baetica* was composed in 1919. This work contains an avant-garde harmony, a sharp rhythm of Flamenco, dark and expressive melody of *Cante Jondo*. It was dedicated to Artur Rubinstein, but Josef Hofmann premiered in 1920 in New York. Rubinstein also performed in New York few days after Hofmann and he introduced this work in London(1922), in Madrid, Malaga, Barcelona(1923) Buenos Aires, Paris(1923), Cadiz(1926).

In 1922, Falla moved to Alhambra, Granada. He visited this place first in 1919, and loved very much. At about that time, Falla was interested in song of Flamenco, *Cante Jondo*. He became a close friend with Garcia Lorca who was well known Andalusian poet and specialist of *Cante Jondo*. Falla and Lorca founded the contest of *Cante Jondo* in 1922, concerned about the decline of tradition of *Cante Jondo*. Falla met well known cembalist Wanda Landowska at that time. In 1923, Falla received a commission from madam Polinac to compose the opera of puppet show, in the title of *El retablo de Maese Pedro*. Libretto was written by Falla himself, based on second act of Don Quixote by Cervantes. It is written for orchestra with solo harpsichord and solo harp. Landowska was involved for the premiere.

Falla spent 4 years for composing *Harpsichord Concerto* which was completed in 1926. This work was commissioned and premiered by Landowska in Palau de la Musica Catalunya in Barcelona.

From 1927 to 1936, Falla wrote very few composition. This was partly due to his health condition and also partly due to taking all the time and effort to compose a large-scale cantata *Atlantida* in Catalan text which is based on the legend of Continent. It was a life-long wish of Falla as a pious Christian to write a mass.

In 1931, there was a right wing uprising in republican Spain and in Granada, too, had an air of unrest. In August of that year the shocking incident occurred that his close friend, great poet Garcia Lorca was suddenly abducted and executed without any reason. Falla was obliged to live quietly in the country side until the cease of civil war. In this period, he composed a piano work *Homenaje : à tombeau de Paul Dukas* upon his respected mentor's death.

In 1939, Falla made journey to Argentine for the concert in Buenos Aires. He never returned to his native country. After moved to Argentine, he concertized and lived in mountain villa in Alta Gracia, the Argentine province of Cordoba. His sister Maria del Carmen devotedly took care of him who was a bachelor throughout his life.

He died on November 14, 1946, a few days before his 70th birthday. In 1947, his remains were brought back to his native Spain by his sister and the funeral took place in the cathedral at Cadiz. The unfinished work *Atlantida* was completed by his favorite pupil, Ernesto Halffter. It was premiered in 1961 at the Liceu Theater in Barcelona. The works of Falla is loved by music lovers as master works which are the fascinating fusion of Spanish nationalism with Classical music. And this tradition is succeeded by Latin American music.

by Dr. Rie HIRAI

● Commentary

2 Danzas Españolas (2 Spanish Dances)
from *La Vida Breve*

La vida breve is an opera which Falla composed in 1904 when he was 27 years old. This work won the 1st prize in a competition, held by Royal Academy of Music in Madrid, among tough competitors. *La vida breve*, in 2 acts, 4 scenes, uses a text in Andalusian dialect, written by famous librettist Carlos Fernandez Shaw. In 1907, Falla went to Paris where he had a very fortunate encounter with Paul Dukas. Dukas was much impressed with the opera *La vida breve* by talented young composer from Spain. He made a great effort to the premiere of this opera to be realized. At last it was premiered in Nice, in April of 1913. Then, at in the Opera Comique of Paris in January, 1914 and in Zaruzuela Theatre in Madrid in November of the same year. By these consequent performances, Falla became widely known as a prominent composer.

The story of the opera is a tragic love story between a lower class gypsy girl and a high class youth.

Both the Two dances appear in the Act 2, No.1 in Scene 1, and No.2 in Scene 2. Both dances are music of wedding in the style of Flamenco songs and dances.

We used the vocal score of *La vida breve* published in Paris in 1913 by Max Eschig, as the base document for our edition.

by Dr. Rie HIRAI

● Performing Suggestions

◆ Danza Española Nº1 (Spanish Dance No.1)
This works must be the first piece of Falla to became internationally known to musical world. Besides the original orchestra version, and piano solo version, it was transcribed for various instrumentation : such as for the band, guitar, violin, cello, piano duo (both 2 pianos and 4-hands) etc. Among these numerous arrangements. The one for violin and piano by Fritz Kreisler is most famous and still widely performed by violinists.

The theme is written in 3/8 meter of quick Flamenco dance. One can hear the sound of castanets and foot stampings of Flamenco dancers. In 4-measure introduction phrase, left hand staccato must be played very sharp while the right hand tremolo should be non legato. The theme must be heard clearly in singing tone in strict tempo.

From M49, the editors recommend playing in non legato touch either with pedal or without pedal.

From M96 where music becomes contrapuntal, use very small amount of pedal.

In **Pesante** section from M115, tempo becomes broadened

and the singing of Cante Jondo appears. The theme must be played in big, round tone from the arm.

Through the entire piece, the small notes need not be played.

◆ Danza Española Nº2 (Spanish Dance No.2)

This dance is written in 3/4 meter using cross rhythm mainly hemiola throughout. Due to pedal notes and wide span of left hand, this piece needs ample use of pedal. Syncopated rhythm is used throughout this piece, make sure to produce a swinging movement.

The double-note scale passage is better to be played in non-legato touch. Bring out the contrapuntal line in the left hand. In **Poco Animato** section, the voice of chorus in octave unison appears. Here, make sure to produce a round forte sound and sing broadly even it has a hemiola rhythm.

At M229, it has a cross rhythm: right hand plays in 3/4 meter while left hand plays in hemiola. The dance gradually accelerate and increasing volume toward the end.

by Dr. Takejiro T. HIRAI and Dr. Rie HIRAI

Danza Española
Nº 1
"La Vida Breve"

スペイン舞曲 第1番
オペラ《はかなき人生》より

Manuel de Falla

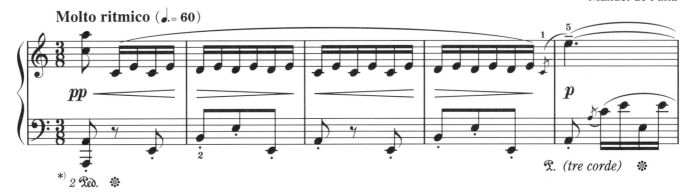

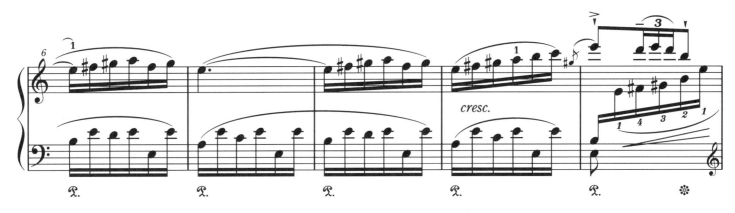

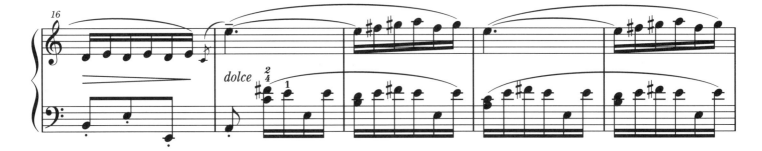

*) 原典に付されたペダル指示で、右のペダルとソフトペダルの両方を使ってという意味。
Original pedaling to use both the damper pedal and una corda pedal.

15

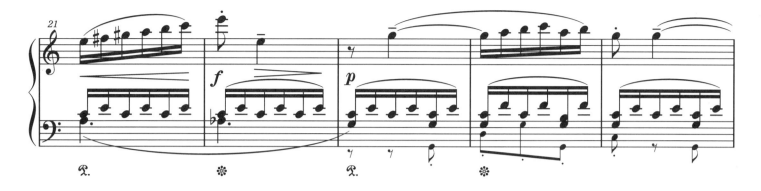

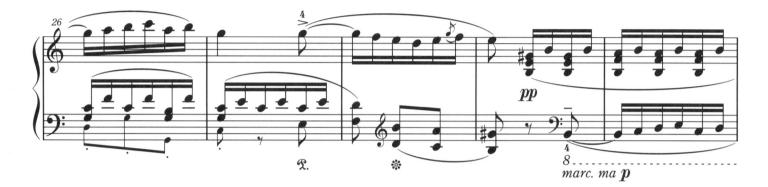

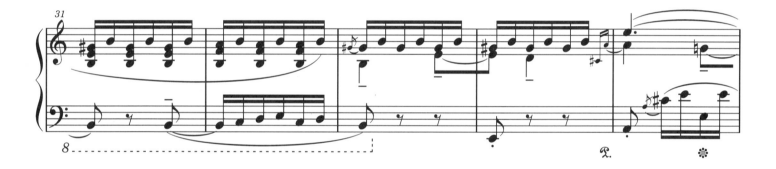

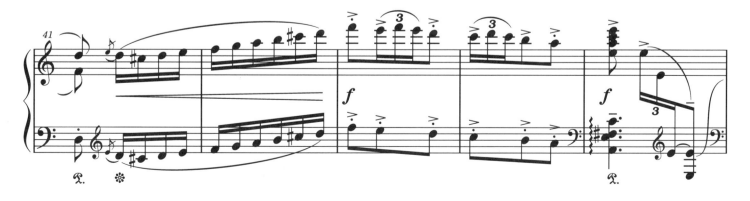

16

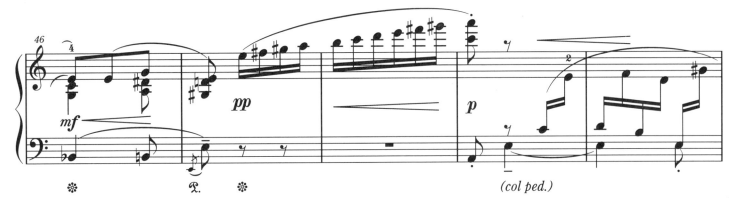

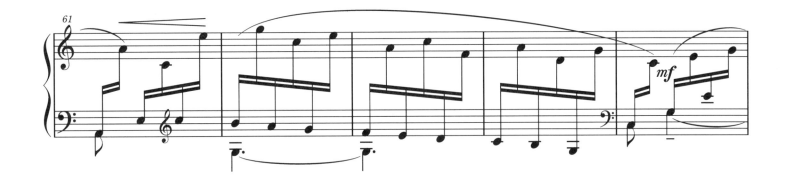

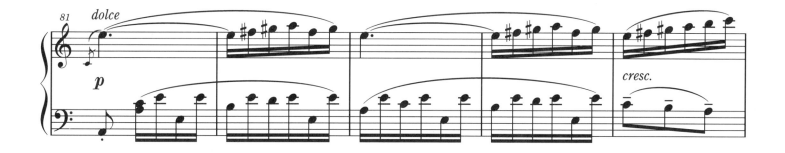

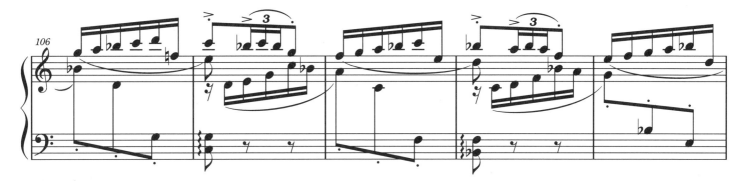

Pesante, ma con fuoco

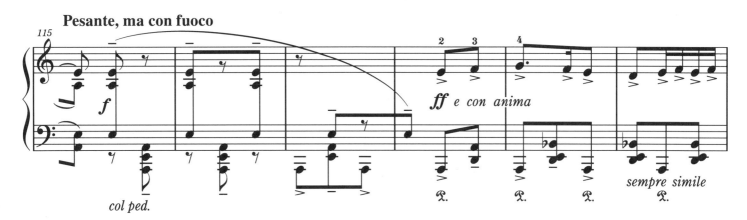

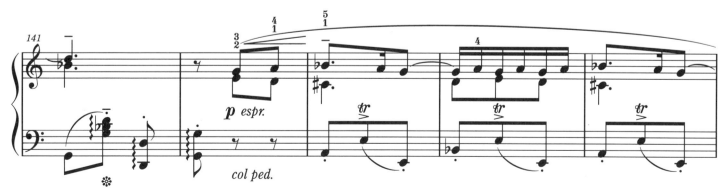

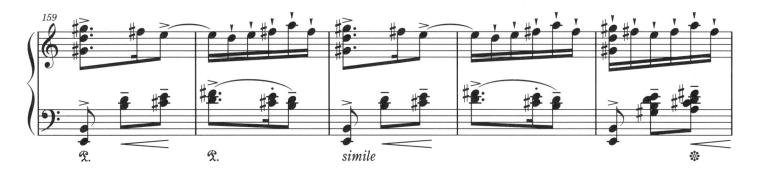

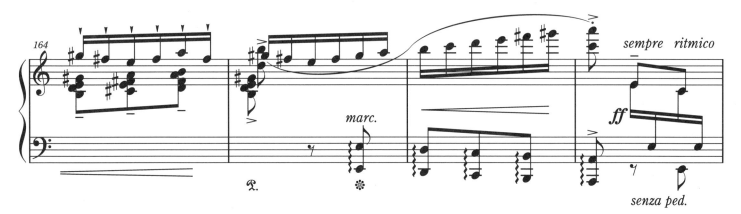

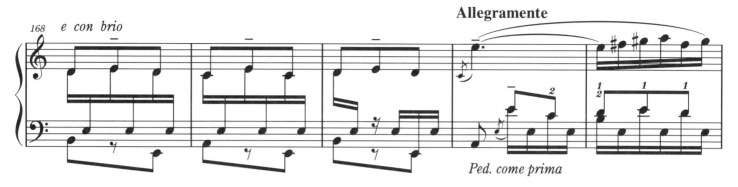

Allegramente

e con brio

Ped. come prima

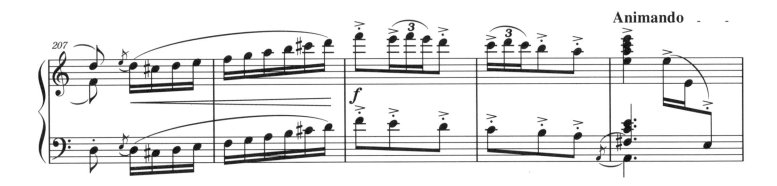

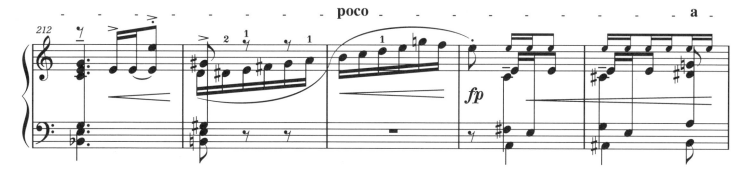

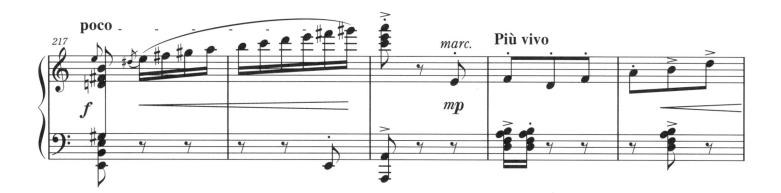

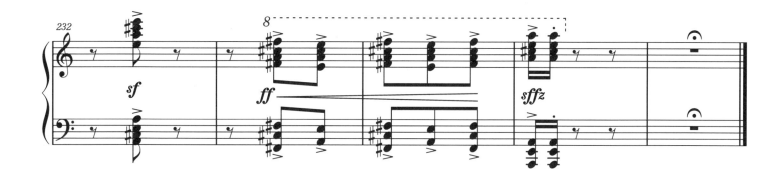

Danza Española
Nº 2
"La Vida Breve"

スペイン舞曲 第 2 番
オペラ《はかなき人生》より

Manuel de Falla

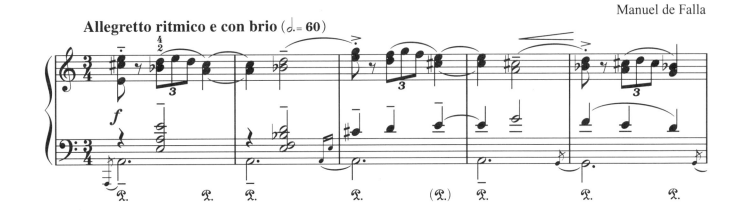

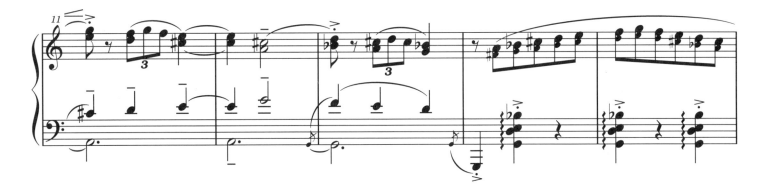

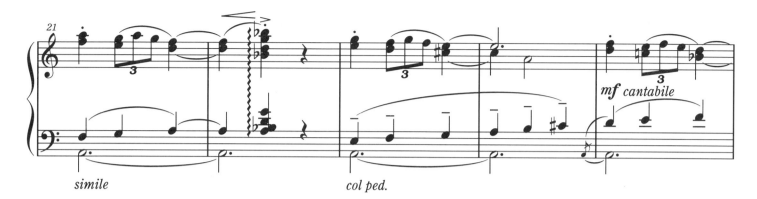

simile   col ped.

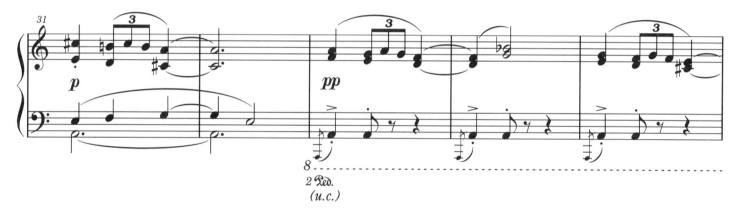

26

A tempo Poco più animato

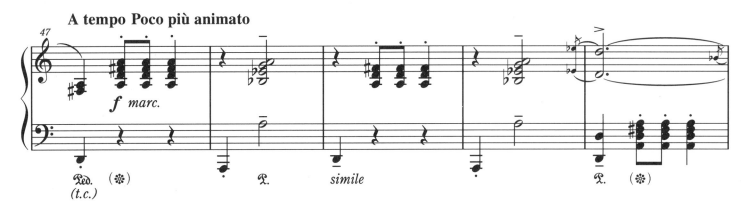

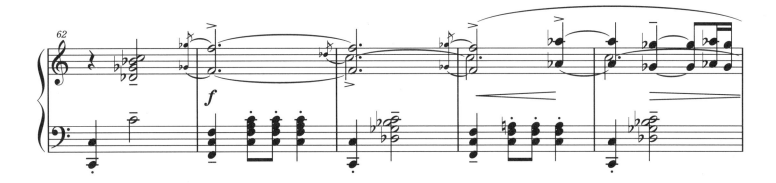

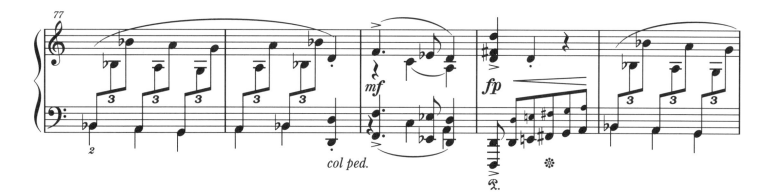

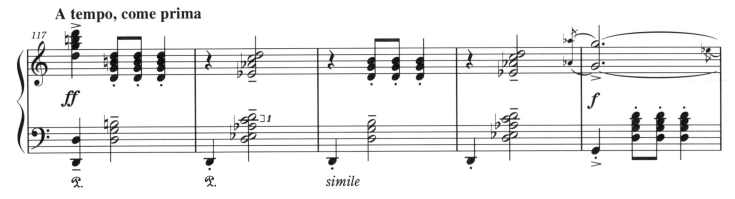

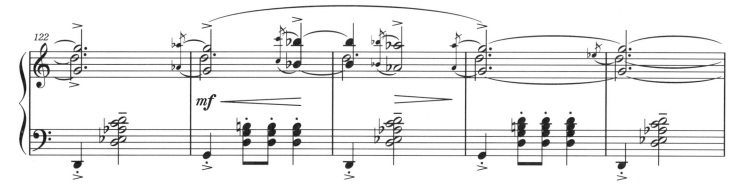

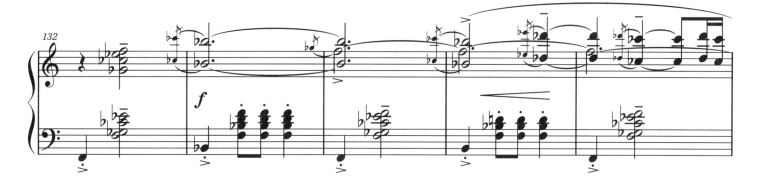
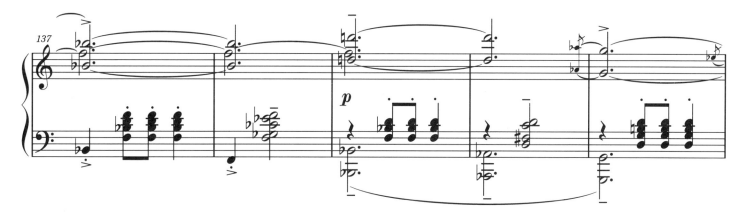

Poco meno vivo

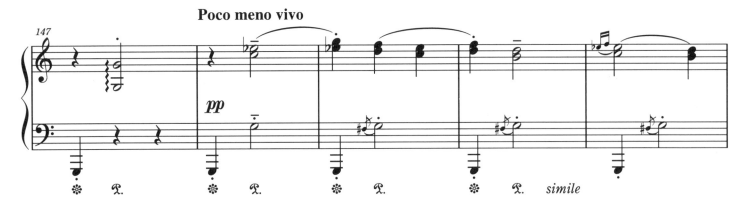

col ped.

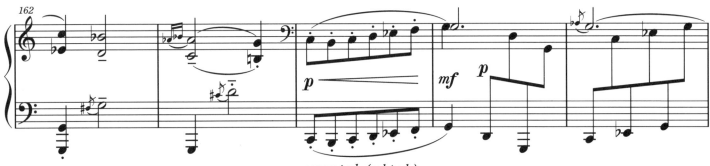
senza ped. (col ped.)

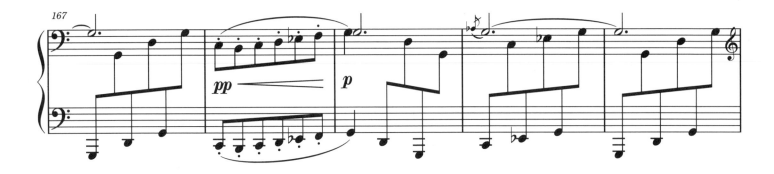

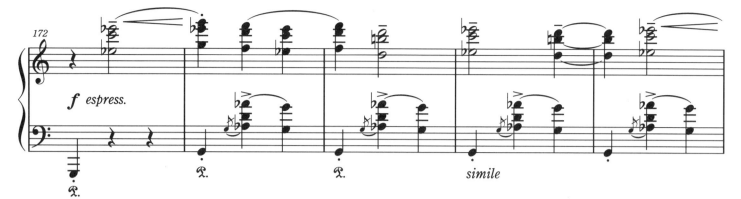

Poco più animato

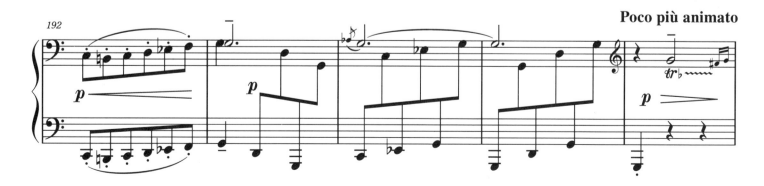

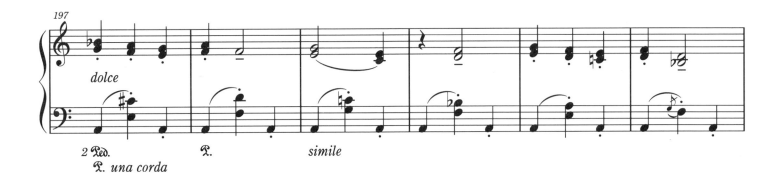

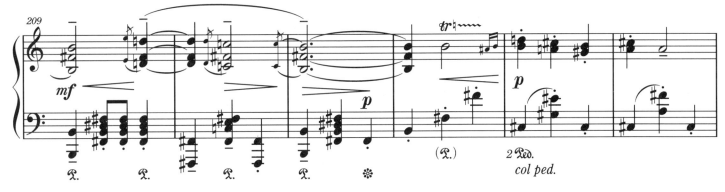

sempre animando, ma gradualmente

Ped. come sopra

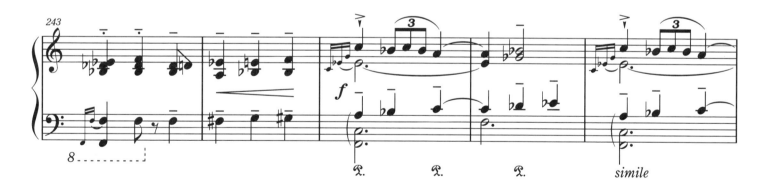

Poco rit.

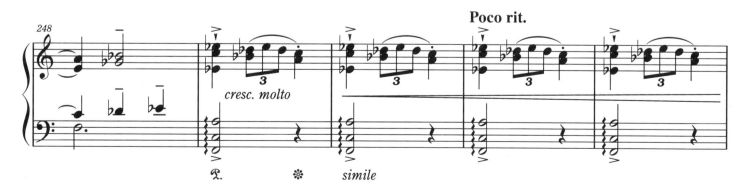

Iº Tempo *sempre animando*

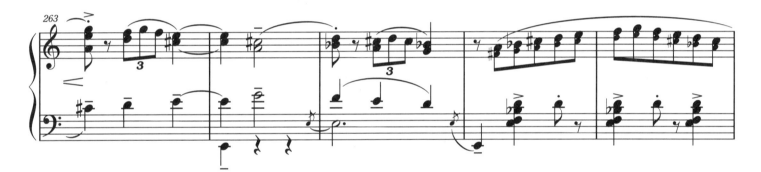

Animato assai

stringendo

■ PROFILE

平井丈二郎（孝知）（ひらいたけじろう〔本名〕たかとも）（ピアニスト）

父・康三郎にピアノと作曲を学び、10歳で自作「主題と変奏」をNHKより放送。永井進氏に師事。1962年東京藝術大学を首席で卒業、安宅賞受賞。1964年同専攻科修了。1967年米国ジュリアード音楽大学留学、S．ゴロドニツキー教授に師事。翌年同大学バルトークコンテストで優勝。1970年ヴィオッティ国際コンクール第2位。1971年ヨーロッパ演奏旅行。1973年ワシントンとニューヨークでデビューし、いずれも絶讃をうけた。1974年学位論文「ロマン派ピアノ音楽の始祖ジョン・フィールド」の発表及び3回のドクター・リサイタル（公開）により、ジュリアード大学より東洋人として初のDMA（音楽芸術博士）の学位を贈られた。1975年帰国後、放送や協奏曲に出演。数々のリサイタルを行い、幅広いレパートリーで、いずれも高い評価をかち得ている。

こうした演奏活動のほか、大阪音楽大学教授、東京藝術大学教授、聖徳大学音楽学部教授、愛知県立芸術大学で教鞭をとり、優秀な若手ピアニストを世におくっている。又、ピアノ曲、歌曲など作曲家としても活動を行っている。全音楽譜出版社より彼の監修・編纂によるジョン・フィールドピアノ名曲選集（1984年）、スクリアビンピアノ曲集全5巻（1987-90年）、ラフマニノフピアノ曲集（2005年-）が出版されている。又、グラナドス（2008年-）及びファリャ（2012年-）ピアノ曲集を平井李枝と編纂・校訂し出版している。東京藝術大学名誉教授。

平井李枝（ひらいりえ）（ピアニスト）

幼少より父・平井丈二郎にピアノ、作曲を師事。東京藝術大学音楽学部附属音楽高等学校を経て東京藝術大学音楽学部器楽科ピアノ専攻卒業。国内外でリサイタルを開催し、ハイドン、ショパン、グリーグ、スクリアビン、ラフマニノフ、グラナドス、ファリャ等、幅広いレパートリーは、「明晰なタッチ、深く含蓄のある音、絶妙なペダル操作、素晴らしい完成度」と高い評価を得ている。またレクチャーコンサートや公開講座、雑誌等への記事や論文の執筆の他、ソプラノ歌手としても活動し、文化庁推薦芸術家として全国の学校でピアノとソプラノによる公演も行っている。2008年スペイン・バルセロナでグラナドスの研究者としてピアノリサイタルを開催。2010年、グラナドスに関する学位論文とリサイタルにより音楽博士の学位を得る。2011年、2012年スペイン・カタロニア政府の招聘によりカタロニア国立図書館でリサイタルを開催。カタロニア国営テレビ、バルセロナテレビに生中継される。2011年2月同図書館より栄誉賞を受賞。2008年よりグラナドス、2012年よりファリャのピアノ曲集を平井丈二郎と編纂・校訂し全音楽譜出版社より出版、また2010年よりラフマニノフピアノ曲集の編纂・校訂に加わる。現在早稲田大学演劇博物館および総合研究機構オペラ研究所招聘研究員。

TAKEJIRO Takatomo HIRAI, pianist, D.M.A. (Juilliard)

Takejiro Hirai is the younger son of noted Japanese composer Professor Kozaburo Hirai. He began his musical education at an early age under his father's tutelage, studying piano, composition and conducting, and at the age of ten performed his own composition, "Theme and Variations for Piano", in a broadcast over NHK, the Japanese national radio network. Following his graduation from Tokyo University of Arts, Takejiro Hirai came to the United States for further study in piano at The Juilliard School with Sascha Gorodnitzki. Here he won the competition to perform Bartok's Third Piano Concerto with the Juilliard Orchestra. He is also winner of the Viotti International Piano Competition of Italy. He made his U.S. debut in Washington D.C. and New York in 1973, which won the highest critic acclaim. He received his Doctor of Musical Arts degree in piano from Juilliard in 1974. His doctoral thesis was entitled "John Field —Pioneer of Romantic Piano Music".

Takejiro Hirai has appeared with orchestras, in recitals and in chamber music concerts in Japan, Europe and the United States. During the years 1967 and 1971 he made extensive tours in Europe. He had been a professor of piano at the Osaka College of Music, Tokyo University of the Arts (Tokyo Geidai), Seitoku University Faculty of Music, and he also had taught at Aichi University of Arts. He is also known as a composer of piano music, art songs and chamber music. He edited Piano Works by John Field (1984), Scriabin in 5 vols. (1987–90), and Rachmaninoff (2005–), Granados (2008–), Falla (2012–), edited with Rie Hirai, published by Zen-On Music Co. Professor Emeritus of Tokyo University of the Arts.

RIE HIRAI, pianist, D.M.

The daughter of Professor Takejiro Hirai. She began studying piano and composition from her father. She graduated from both the High School Division and the Department of the Tokyo University of the Arts (GEIDAI). She is giving many recitals in Japan and overseas. Among her large repertoires, Haydn, Chopin, Grieg, Scriabin, Rachmaninoff, Granados, Falla are highly estimated by the critic as "Most clear touch", "Deep Expressive Tone", "Remarkable perfection, which shows wide capacity of expression".

Rie Hirai holds lecture concerts, wrote articles and research thesis on musical journals. She is also active as soprano singer holding a concert of piano and soprano for public schools around Japan sponsored by Minister of Culture. In 2008, she gave a recital in Barcelona, Spain as a Granados scholar. She received her Doctor of Music degree in 2010 with the doctoral thesis on the piano works of Granados. In 2011 and 2012, she gave recitals in Barcelona by invitation of Biblioteca Nacional de Catalunya. And this concerts were televised by Catalan National Television and Barcelona TV. She received prize of honor from the Biblioteca.

She edited Piano Works of Granados(2008–), Manuel de Falla(2012–) with Takejiro Hirai, published by Zen-On Music Co. In 2010, she joined as co-editor of Rachmaninoff Piano works.

Presently, she is fellow of The TSUBOUCHI Memorial Theatre Museum and opera project in Waseda University.

ファリャ：スペイン舞曲 第1番・第2番
《はかなき人生》より
校訂・解説 ———————— 平井丈二郎・平井李枝
第1版第1刷発行 ———————— 2012年5月15日

発行 —— 株式会社全音楽譜出版社
———— 東京都新宿区上落合2丁目13番3号〒161-0034
———— TEL・営業部03・3227-6270
出版部03・3227-6280
URL http://www.zen-on.co.jp/
ISBN978-4-11-124492-8

1205098